ncR

NOV 1 4 1981

NOV 3 0 1985

MAR 7 1982

MAY 3 1 1982

NOV 1 3 1982

FEB 2 7 1983

NOV 3 0 1983

MAR 3 1984

APR 6 1984

FEB 9 1986

3

PROVERBS OF MANY NATIONS

PROVERBS
of many
NATIONS

Compiled and illustrated by
EMERY KELEN

LOTHROP, LEE & SHEPARD CO., INC. • NEW YORK

ACKNOWLEDGMENT

I am greatly indebted to Lieutenant Colonel V.S.M. de Guinzbourg, who compiled and published WIT AND WISDOM OF THE UNITED NATIONS.

E. K.

CONTENTS

CONTENTS

INTRODUCTION

A proverb is age-old wisdom stated in a few words. People differ in the color of their skin, their costumes, their traditions, but they express wisdom in similar ways: only the setting varies. While the European speaks of oaks and horses, the African talks of palm trees and camels, and the Asian of bamboo and buffalos.

But the message is the same, for the wisdom of this world is one and indivisible, and it is the common treasure of all the world's people.

PROVERBS OF MANY NATIONS

Time passes away, but sayings remain. (TAMIL: INDIA AND CEYLON)

Learn proverbs well and good speech will come naturally. (CHINESE)

There are no people a thousand years old, but there are words a thousand years old. (INNER MONGOLIAN)

DEEDS COUNT, NOT WORDS

No stomach is satisfied by good words. (NORWEGIAN)

Talk does not cook rice. (CHINESE)

Handsome words don't butter cabbage. (GERMAN)

All talk is no cider. (AMERICAN)

It is one thing to cackle and another to lay an egg.
(ECUADORIAN)

TOO LATE!

Locking the barn door
after the horse is gone.
(AMERICAN)

The fire engines arrive after
the house has burned down.
(GERMAN)

After the wedding, we don't need music. (TARTAR)

After the rain, there's no need for an umbrella.
(BULGARIAN)

WHAT'S DONE IS DONE

You can't unscramble eggs. (AMERICAN)

No use crying over spilt milk. (ENGLISH)

What can't be cured must be endured. (ITALIAN)

An army that has crossed the river can't turn back.
(MALAGASY REPUBLIC: AFRICA)

DON'T MAKE THE SAME MISTAKES

Never too late to mend. (SPANISH)

It is better to have trouble at the beginning than at the end. (TELUGU: INDIA)

No matter how far you have gone on a wrong road, turn back. (TURKISH)

It is better to turn back than to get lost. (RUSSIAN)

WAIT AND SEE

Do not bless the fish until you land it. (IRISH)

Don't count your chickens
before they are hatched.
(AMERICAN)

Having heard talk about a bath, he undressed in the
street. (ARABIC)

The baby is not yet born, and you say his nose is like his
grandfather's. (PUNJABI: INDIA)

Sometimes the canoe sinks before it reaches the shore.
(CAMEROONS: AFRICA)

QUARRELS SERVE OTHERS

When two quarrel, the third rejoices. (SPANISH)

It is the buyer who profits from the fight of two shop-
keepers. (KOREAN)

While the snipe and the mussel struggled with each
other, the fisherman caught them both. (CHINESE)

While dogs fight among themselves,
the wolf devours the sheep.
(HUNGARIAN)

POOR EXCUSES

The bad worker blames his tools.
  (AMERICAN)

The singer covers up the wrong note with a cough.
  (GERMAN)

The archer who misses has a lie ready. (SPANISH)

He who does not want to pray says the door of the mosque
  is closed. (ARABIC)

If the fish had not opened its mouth, it would not have been caught. (MEXICAN)

There is no shame in keeping silent if you have nothing to say. (RUSSIAN)

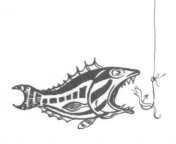

Flies don't enter a closed mouth. (ITALIAN)

HOW RUMORS SPREAD

One dog barks because it sees something; a hundred dogs
    bark because they heard the first dog bark.
    (CHINESE)

If you pull one pig by the tail,
all the rest squeal.
    (DUTCH)

One rooster wakens all the roosters in the village.
    (GERMAN)

If you kick one walnut in the sack, all the rest clatter.
    (HUNGARIAN)

He who grabs too much holds fast but little. (SPANISH)

The dog who goes to many weddings eats at none. (MEXICAN)

Don't run after the wild boar and lose the pig at home. (CHINESE)

The magpie wants more than its tail can carry. (HUNGARIAN)

YOU MUST CHOOSE

You can't have your cake and eat it too. (AMERICAN)

If you want the hen's egg, you must put up with her cackling. (ENGLISH)

One can't make the bed and save the sheet. (FRENCH)

There's no catching trout with dry breeches. (PORTUGUESE)

Don't bite off more than you can chew. (AMERICAN)

Fit your stocking to your foot. (FRENCH)

Stretch your arm no farther than your sleeve. (ENGLISH)

Be sure to keep an eye out for what you can swallow—
and also for what can swallow you. (TELUGU: INDIA)

RECOGNIZE YOUR SHORTCOMINGS

One donkey calls another Longears. (SPANISH)

The pot calls the kettle black. (AMERICAN)

The coal is making fun of the cinder. (KENYA: AFRICA)

The sieve says to the needle: You have a hole in your tail. (PAKISTANI)

The fool says to the fool: You are a fool. (GUINEA: AFRICA)

To hide one lie, a thousand lies are needed. (TELUGU: INDIA)

The liar is caught more quickly than a limping dog. (HUNGARIAN)

He who lied yesterday will not be believed tomorrow. (RUSSIAN)

Trust not a man who lies *for* you, for he may lie *to* you. (ARABIC)

If you lie and eat fish at the same time, you'd better be careful. You might swallow a bone, and get into trouble. (COSTA RICAN)

TRUTH

Truth will out. (AMERICAN)

A needle wrapped in a rag will be found in the end.
(VIETNAMESE)

Time will discover the truth. (COLOMBIAN)

The crime was committed in the bush, but it is now
talked about on the highway. (SAMOAN)

The tail of the fox will show
no matter how hard
he tries to hide it.
(HUNGARIAN)

If you chase two hares, you will not catch either.
(RUSSIAN)

He who carries two melons in one hand is sure to drop
at least one of them. (ARABIC)

A man cannot whistle and drink at the same time.
(ENGLISH, DANISH)

You cannot hold onto two cows' tails at once. (UPPER
VOLTA: AFRICA)

CAUSE AND EFFECT

There's no smoke without fire. (ENGLISH, CZECH)

If nothing touches the bamboo tree, it does not make a sound. (EWE TRIBE, SOUTH GHANA: AFRICA)

An old crow does not croak for nothing. (RUSSIAN)

Nobody cries who has not been pinched. (KIKUYU TRIBE, KENYA: AFRICA)

VALUE WHAT YOU HAVE

A bird in the hand is worth two in the bush. (AMERICAN)

It's better to have a sparrow today than a wild turkey
tomorrow. (HUNGARIAN)

A penny in the pocket is worth ten outside of it.
(LEBANESE)

GET AN EARLY START

The morning hour has gold in its mouth. (GERMAN)

Early to bed, early to rise,
Makes a man healthy, wealthy, and wise. (ENGLISH)

The early bird catches the worm.
    (AMERICAN)

LEARN WHILE YOU'RE YOUNG

What Johnny learned, John will do. (GERMAN)

Young man idle and old man needy.
(ITALIAN)

What is learned in the cradle lasts till the grave.
(HUNGARIAN)

32

BAD MOVES

To jump from the frying pan into the fire. (AMERICAN)

He ran away from the wolf only to meet the bear.
    (RUSSIAN)

Do not seek to escape from the flood by clinging to a
    tiger's tail. (CHINESE)

To hit a policeman over the head and then to take refuge
    with the sheriff. (SPANISH)

To jump into the water to escape the rain. (FRENCH)

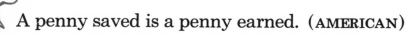

A penny saved is a penny earned. (AMERICAN)

Add pence to pence
For wealth comes hence. (ENGLISH)

Who heeds not a penny
Shall never have any. (SCOTTISH)

That man's purse will never be bare
Who knows when to buy, to spend, and to spare.
    (GERMAN)

MAKING A PURCHASE

Never buy a pig in a poke. (AMERICAN)

Taste and try
Before you buy. (ENGLISH)

Even an earthen jar should be tested before purchasing.
(SINDHI: INDIA)

Don't buy a cat in a sack. (HUNGARIAN)

DON'T RUSH THINGS!

Haste makes waste. (AMERICAN)

Do not hurry, do not flurry,
Nothing good is got by worry. (ENGLISH)

Hasty work is seldom good. (FINNISH)

To catch the monkey requires
patience. (SENEGAL: AFRICA)

TAKE YOUR TIME

Step by step one ascends the staircase. (TURKISH)

Lick by lick the cow ate the grindstone. (AMERICAN—
    TEXAS)

Word by word great books are written. (ITALIAN)

Little strokes fell great oaks. (ENGLISH)

Little by little the cotton thread becomes a loincloth.
    (DAHOMEY: AFRICA)

A stitch in time saves nine. (AMERICAN)

A lazy man works twice. (NORWEGIAN)

Never put off till tomorrow what you can do today. (GERMAN)

HELP YOURSELF

God gives food to the birds, but they must look for it.
(GERMAN)

The ripest fruit will not fall into your mouth. (CHINESE)

Nothing falls into the mouth of a sleeping fox.
(HUNGARIAN)

TAKE ADVANTAGE OF OPPORTUNITY

Strike while the iron is hot. (ENGLISH, GERMAN)

Make hay while the sun shines. (AMERICAN)

Make haste about it if it is a good thing. (JAPANESE)

A man who misses his chance, and a monkey who misses his branch, cannot be helped. (HINDUSTANI: INDIA)

FOLLOW THROUGH

If you have to kill a snake, kill it once and for all.
(JAPANESE)

Do not hold the leopard's tail, but if you hold it, don't let
it go. (AMHARIC: ETHIOPIA)

Once you have said, "Here I am," don't try to say that
you are not there. (HAITIAN)

Whoever lies down with a dog will get up with fleas.
　　(HEBREW)

He who mixes with garbage ought not to be astonished
　　if pigs devour him. (SERBIAN: YUGOSLAVIA)

He who gets into cracked corn will be eaten by hogs.
　　(HUNGARIAN)

The leopard never changes its spots. (AMERICAN)

A wolf remains a wolf even if it has not devoured your sheep. (MONGOLIAN)

Pound the water and it is still water. (SAUDI ARABIAN)

BRAGGING

Every man thinks his own geese are swans. (ENGLISH)

Every gypsy praises his own horse. (HUNGARIAN)

Nobody calls his own buttermilk sour. (IRANIAN)

Every peddler praises his needles. (SPANISH)

TAKING RESPONSIBILITY

You have cooked the broth, now spoon it out. (RUSSIAN)

As you have made your bed, so you must lie in it. (FRENCH)

He who ate the nuts must sweep away the shells. (GERMAN)

AFTER SOMETHING'S LOST

You ought to have seen the fish that got away!
    (AMERICAN, TURKISH)

The knife that was lost had a golden haft. (UZBEK: SOVIET
    UNION)

The cow that was stolen used to give four pails of milk.
    (HUNGARIAN)

47

He gives twice who gives quickly. (ITALIAN)

Charity begins at home. (AMERICAN)

Charity is not wasted, even if you are not thanked for it. (HUNGARIAN)

Don't make gratitude the price of charity. (IRANIAN)

ONE GOOD TURN DESERVES ANOTHER

Roll my log and I'll roll yours. (AMERICAN)

One hand washes the other. (AMERICAN)

You amuse my child, and I'll take care of your old father.
   (HINDUSTANI: INDIA)

50

HUNGER

When one eats and the other looks on, there is likely to be a fight. (TURKISH)

He who is starving hates him who is eating. (GABON: AFRICA)

The hungry will not fall asleep because someone else has enough to eat. (SWAHILI, ZANZIBAR: AFRICA)

INNOCENT VICTIMS

When elephants battle, the ants perish. (CAMBODIAN)

When lizards eat pepper, it is the frog that perspires.
(GHANA: AFRICA)

When buffalos battle, the grass is trampled down.
(LAOTIAN)

The horses were fighting each other, but it was the donkey who got kicked. (ARABIC)

WAR

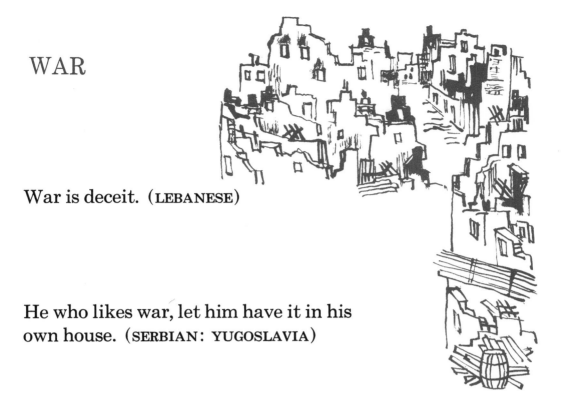

War is deceit. (LEBANESE)

He who likes war, let him have it in his
own house. (SERBIAN: YUGOSLAVIA)

In war, you become ashes if you lose—and charcoal if
you win. (MALAYSIAN)

Even the winner of a war
suffers from lack of bread.
(CZECH)

Anger is a bad adviser. (HUNGARIAN)

He got angry with the rat and set fire to the house. (PAKISTANI)

He got angry with the fleas and threw his fur coat into the oven. (RUSSIAN)

If you kick a stone because you are angry at it, you will only hurt your foot. (KOREAN)

THE POWER OF GENTLE WORDS

Fair speech turns elephants away from the garden path.
(SWAHILI: AFRICA)

With soft words, one may talk a serpent out of its hole.
(IRANIAN)

Good words cost nothing. (GERMAN, SWEDISH, SPANISH, HUNGARIAN)

Gentle words open iron gates. (BULGARIAN)

EQUALITY

Ask me what is my virtue, not what is the color of my skin. (ARABIC)

White or black, we are human. (SPANISH)

You should not hate everyone who has a different nose than you. (GERMAN)

The world belongs to the whole world. (JAPANESE)

A friend in need is a friend indeed. (AMERICAN)

Get to know new friends, but don't forget the old ones. (BULGARIAN)

You cannot buy a friend with money. (RUSSIAN)

A handful of friends is better than a wagon of gold. (SLOVAK: CZECHOSLOVAKIA)

DISAGREEMENT AMONG FRIENDS

Even the ladle and the cooking pot collide.
   (MALAYSIAN)

The tooth often bites the tongue, and yet they stay together. (GERMAN)

A friend's frown is better than a fool's smile. (HEBREW)

Love your friend together with his fault. (ITALIAN)

A quarrel with a friend is like pepper in the food—it makes the friendship stronger. (HUNGARIAN)

One finger cannot lift a pebble. (IRANIAN)

One bell does not make a concert. (ITALIAN)

A single bamboo pole does not make a raft. (CHINESE)

STRONG WHEN UNITED

Helping each other, even boys
can hold back a lion.
  (ETHIOPIAN)

United we stand, divided we fall. (AMERICAN)

Unity among the small makes the lion lie down hungry.
  (SWAHILI, ZANZIBAR: AFRICA)

Rich together, poor if separated. (LAOTIAN)

United, even the weak are strong. (GERMAN)

"They shall beat their swords into plowshares, and their spears into pruning hooks; nation shall not lift up sword against nation, neither shall they learn war any more."

PEACE

Better to have bread in peace than a fat calf in war.
(HUNGARIAN)

He who wants to live in peace should not disturb it.
(DANISH)

Even if you have the strength of an elephant and the
paws of a lion, peace is better than war. (IRANIAN)

Peace is more valuable than gold. (FINNISH)

1   2   3   4   5   70   69   68   67   66